Welcome, foolish mortals, to our strange and creepy
compendium of ghastly gags and creature features,
as Beano and The Dandy, and their chilling chums,
entertain us with tales of terror and mystery! Haunting
these pages you'll find relics from DC Thomson's
funny papers archives. This collection will trick or
treat you to classic strips from Dennis and Gnasher,
Desperate Dan, Minnie the Minx — alongside their more
supernatural pals like Winnie the Witch, Number 13,
Hyde and Shriek, and more!

This necronomi-comic of ghoulish guffaws is no mere
collection of monster fun! While you get goosebumps
and a shiver runs up your spine, behold the beastly
beautiful artwork of some of Britain's top artists,
whose comic illustrations are brought back to life like
Frankenstein's monster himself!

Enjoy... for there's no turning back now!

A Beano Studios Product © DC Thomson Ltd 2022
D.C. Thomson and Co. Ltd.,
185 Fleet Street,
London EC4A 2HS.

Printed in the EU.

ISBN: 9781845359034

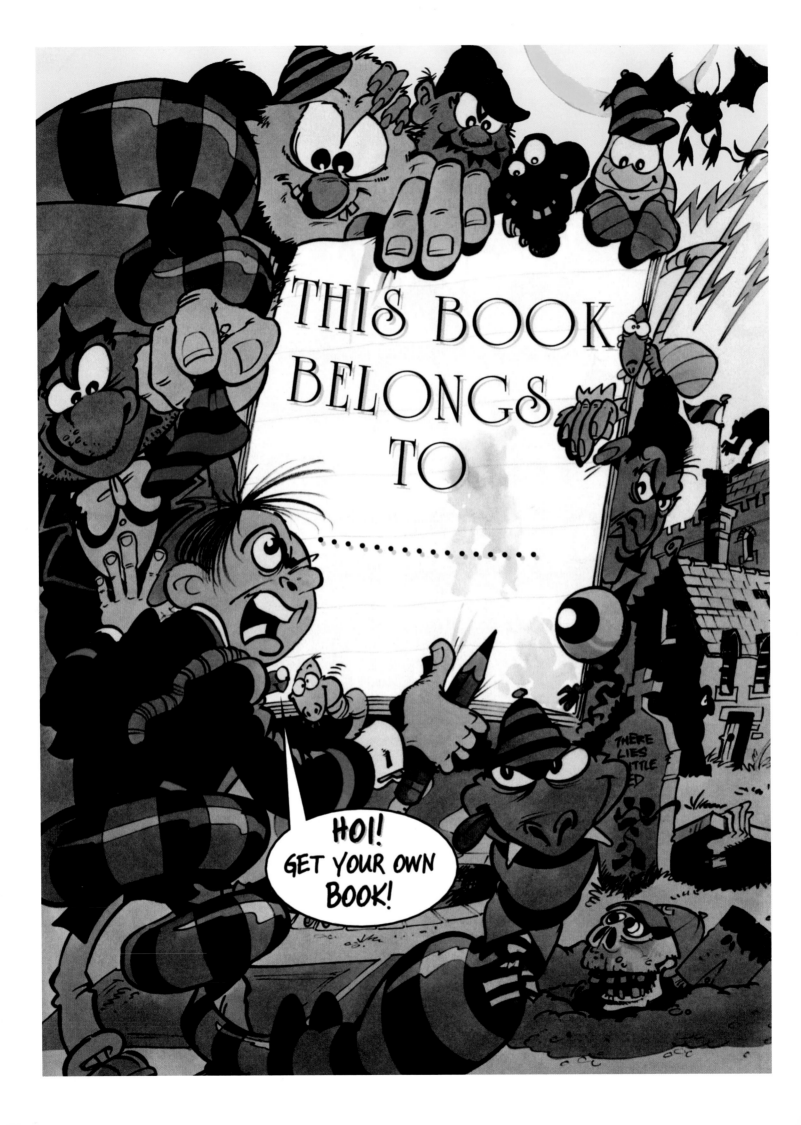

MICKEY'S MAGIC BOOK

Hansel and Gretel's was the sweetest little house Mickey had ever seen. Then the Witch appeared and Mickey didn't know which way to turn.

Winnie the Witch

ACROSS the sky see Winnie zoom,
Perched safely on her magic broom.
She's on the scent with her big snitch
For some poor person to bewitch.

She soars across the chimney stack,
When something hits our poor witch—smack !
A sweep's at work. Up his brush flies
And sweeps our Winnie from the skies.

Now Winnie Witch is black and blue,
And she wants her revenge. Too true !
She says a spell, for she has planned
To make the chimney pot expand.

The chimney's big and deep and fat.
Oh, gosh ! The poor sweep won't like that !
'Twill take him days, the poor old man,
To get that chimney spick and span.

The sweep won't take this lying down,
And soon it's Winnie's turn to frown.
Before our witch has time to grouse,
The sweep runs her into the house.

Here is a sight that must be seen—
Win's broomstick sweeps the chimney clean.
Straight up the chimney see her race,
A big scowl on her sooty face.

WINNIE THE WITCH

Winnie goes to Willie's house
And buys some magic brew.
To change a person to a mouse
Is what she wants to do.

Then Winnie takes the magic spell.
She shakes the contents twice,
Then pours it in the townsfolk's well.
Now they'll all change to mice.

But Billy Goat is watching Winn,
And, as she's bending low,
He butts her and she tumbles in,
Down to the foot she'll go.

Then from the well quite suddenly
A little mouse jumps out,
And by its small peaked hat you'll see
It's Winn without a doubt.

Winn's cat then licks his lips in joy
And chases her full speed.
But Willie Wizard spoils his ploy,
And helps Winn in her need.

Still down the street see Winnie go,
And Willie laughs, "That's queer.
Her black cat doesn't seem to know
She is herself, I fear."

WINNIE the WITCH

HERE'S Winnie at the starting post,
　All set to run a mile.
"I'll use a spell," hear our witch boast,
　"To help me win in style."

They're off! And Winnie's out in front.
　She's grinning happily.
The rest, due to her magic stunt,
　All run the other way.

"Old Winnie's first!" the mayor cries.
　"The tuck is hers. Hooray!"
Just look at Winnie's greedy eyes.
　She'll have a feast to-day.

Off Winnie goes before they find
　She worked a magic spell.
Though it's a trick, Win doesn't mind.
　She thinks that she's done well.

The victims of the magic spell
　Are running backwards still.
They all crash into Win pell-mell,
　And make her hamper spill.

The copper thinks Win's picnicking,
　And puts her in a cell.
The runners laugh like anything.
　They get the cakes. All's well!

✕ 👤 TOM THUMB The Brave Little One

TOM THUMB, the little boy only six inches high, and his equally tiny friend Tinkel, were one day seated not far from a tiny cottage where an old witch lived. Beside the cottage sat a giant wash-tub about twice as big as the cottage. Tom and Tinkel noticed that the witch was speaking to a man with a horse and cart. Then she pointed to the tiny pair and handed the **man** some money.

As Tom and Tinkel gazed, the man cracked his whip and lead his horse and cart towards them. They jumped down from their perch and started walking towards the witch's tub. Just then the carter passed by and intentionally wheeled his cart through a pool of water, splashing Tom and Tinkel with mud from head to foot.

When the carter had gone, the witch came up to them and said, "I will wash your clothes in my big tub over there."

"Oh thank you," cried Tom.

"Ha," laughed the witch. "You must pay me sixpence before I will do it."

"All right," said Tom, "we must get clean. Here's our money. Now wash our things."

Grinning greedily, the witch lead them to the tub where Tom handed her his clothes. She placed them in a basket and by means of a rope on a pulley raised them into the tub.

"But how will they get washed?" Tom asked.

"Ha, ha, never mind," snarled the witch. "Be thankful they're clean, and ask no questions."

The witch went off and sat down to sleep, but Tom and Tinkel were worried.

"I've a plan," Tinkel exclaimed, after a few moments silence. "Look, the old witch has unhooked the basket and the hook is within reach. You sit on it and I will pull you up, so that you can see what is inside the tub." Tom agreed, and they proceeded to carry out their plan.

"Oh," gasped Tom, "what a wicked witch!"

No wonder Tom was surprised, for there in the tub were several boys and girls washing and ironing clothes.

"What are you doing?" he cried.

"The witch captured us and now she makes us work for her day and night. If we don't, she turns the water on us."

But something had warned the cunning old witch that all was not well, for she climbed her ladder leading to the tub and gazed over the edge. "So that's their trick," she snarled. "I'll teach them to mind their own affairs. If that little brat hadn't interfered he and Tinkel would have been all right. I'll teach them." With that she pressed the lever beside her.

Suddenly a terrible rushing noise filled the air and water spurted from a pipe in the tub. Quickly the tub filled with water, and the children struggled to keep their heads clear. Tinkel, from the outside had seen the witch climb up the ladder, and had scrambled through the overflow pipe. He now swam quickly under water to where Tom sat.

"Tom," he called softly. "Follow me down this way and we will save the children yet." Tom slid from his perch on the mangle and followed Tinkel with swift strokes down to the overflow pipe. Swish—he landed bang on the ground. Tinkel followed a moment after. Picking themselves up they looked round to see if the witch had noticed them.

The witch was busy stirring the water in her tub with her broom-stick, however, and did not notice them.

"Quick," cried Tinkel. "We'll carry this saw up the ladder and saw some of the rungs almost through."

Slowly and quietly they lifted the saw up and started to saw through one spar. When it was almost through they started on the next.

When Tom and Tinkel had sawn three they climbed down and waited for results. After some time the witch took the broom from the tub, and with a ringing cackle she started to descend the ladder. When she came to the cracked rungs her feet went through, her hat flew off, her broom fell, and down to the ground with an awful thud came the witch.

The witch knocked her head on the pole and lay still. Tom and Tinkel rushed off to get help, and when they returned she had not recovered. The soldiers who had come to their aid carried off the witch as a prisoner. Others rescued the children, and then set about destroying the wash-tub.

"Hurrah," cheered Tom and all the children together. "Now we are free to go home and be safe."

PAST SCARING

Lord Knumskull didn't think the gang much good at counting, but they were
able to figure a way of paying him out.

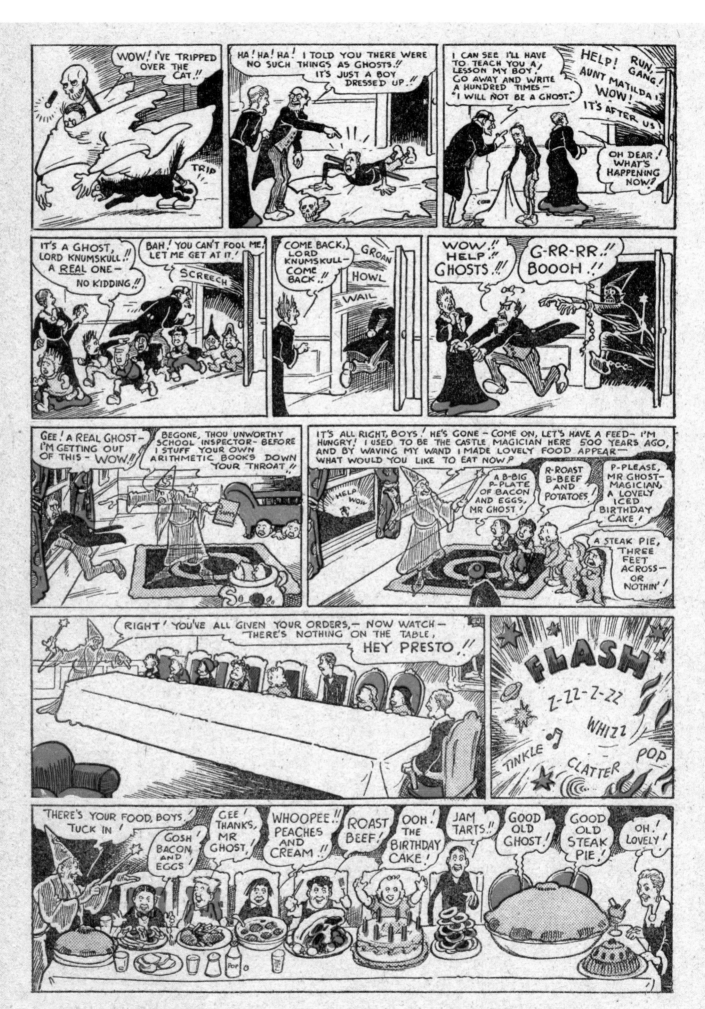

Later the real ghost entered into the spirit of the thing, and then, of course, old Knumskull just didn't stand the ghost of a chance.

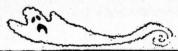

THE TERROR OF CRANBY CASTLE

The Haunted Castle

BERYL whooped with joy when she heard that Miss Primm, the history teacher, was to take the class on a visit to Cranby Castle, which was very old and said to be haunted.

Miss Primm hastily explained that the trip was intended only for those who were keen history students —but she couldn't put Beryl off that way!

"I'm *very* interested in old castles an' knights an' battle-axes an' things," declared Beryl enthusiastically. "I wouldn't miss this for *anything*."

Miss Primm desperately hoped that Beryl might catch measles or something before the day of the trip, but her luck was out. Beryl turned up with the rest of the class, beaming cheerfully.

"I want all of you to keep together and be on your best behaviour," sighed Miss Primm, without much hope, as the class trooped over the creaking drawbridge into the gloomy entrance of the castle. "Mr Widge, the chief guide, is going to show us round."

Mr Widge, who wore a dark suit and a peaked cap, was a rather sour-looking man. Beryl upset him right at the start, for just inside the castle entrance stood an ancient suit of armour holding an upraised mace, and she accidentally jogged it with her elbow.

The armour wobbled and the arm holding the mace suddenly dropped. *Dong!* The mace landed on the guide's head with a thud that nearly knocked him silly.

"Oooo!" he shrieked, glaring furiously at Beryl. "What do you think you're doing?"

"I didn't do anythin'," protested Beryl indignantly. "Kin I help it if your old mace fell down? I didn't put the thing in that silly place, did I? Kin I help it if your head got in the way—?"

"Don't touch anything else in this castle!" roared the guide. Scowling, he rubbed the bump on his head and replaced his dented cap. "Follow me, all of you! First I'll show you the famous tapestry."

The tapestry hung on one of the walls. It was of enormous size and Mr Widge halted under it and pointed up proudly.

"This tapestry is a famous relic of history," he boomed. "It has hung on this wall since the days of good Queen Bess, and is hundreds of years old."

That sounded a very tall story to Beryl. Suspicious, she grabbed at the tapestry and gave it a tug, just to see if it would fall apart.

It didn't fall apart, but it broke loose from its fastenings and dropped from the wall—falling right over the whole class, Miss Primm and the guide.

"That was you again!" spluttered Mr Widge, glowering purple-faced at Beryl, when everybody had at last managed to crawl out from under the tapestry. "Didn't I tell you to leave things alone?"

"Kin I help it if the old thing wasn't hung up properly?" demanded Beryl warmly. "If it's been up there hundreds of years, I'm not surprised it fell down."

The guide breathed hard, but before he could say anything, Miss Primm suddenly grabbed his arm. She was looking rather nervous.

"I—I thought I heard a clanking noise from

She is a queer sight—dressed as a knight.

somewhere behind that wall," she gulped.

"It must have been the ghost," growled Mr Widge. "This castle is said to be haunted by the White Knight, who was killed in a tournament in the fourteenth century. The place is full of secret passages and I'm always hearing clankings and rattlings. Very mysterious it is sometimes."

Miss Primm went a little paler and said no more about the matter, but the news that there were secret passages in the castle made Beryl prick her ears up. She decided that she would slip away from the rest of the class and do a bit of exploring on her own.

"Explorin' secret passages is more fun than lookin' at dusty old tapestries an' things," Beryl muttered to herself.

The rest of the party dutifully followed Mr Widge, but Beryl tip-toed round a corner and wandered around the castle by herself, hopefully hunting for secret passages.

The Ghost Walks

BERYL didn't find any secret passages, but she came across a small suit of armour standing in a dim corner.

"That would just about fit me," she grinned, her eyes gleaming gleefully.

Beryl had often wondered what a knight must have felt like in his tin suit, and this seemed to be her chance

"A headless ghost!" screeched Miss Primm. "It's the ghost of the White Knight!" But it wasn't—it was just Beryl!

to find out. In a few minutes she had buckled on the armour and was clanking along one of the stone passages in it.

Although the armour was small, it was still too big and heavy for Beryl. She could hardly walk. She hadn't taken many steps when the helmet fell off.

The suit being too big for her, Beryl's head was below the neck level of the armour and it looked as if she had no head at all! And to make things even more startling, she picked up the helmet and tucked it under her arm.

Just then, unfortunately, Mr Widge and the rest of the party came round a corner of the passage. They stopped dead at the sight of the headless armoured figure. Miss Primm nearly fainted.

"A headless ghost!" she screeched in horror. "It's the ghost of the White Knight!"

The whole party would have fled in panic if Beryl hadn't tripped up just then. The armour crashed on the stone floor with a ringing clang, and the howl that came from it certainly didn't sound like a ghost.

"It's that girl again!" hooted Mr Widge in fury. "She's a proper menace!"

"I'll see that she is dealt with severely when we get back to school," promised the indignant teacher. "I'll report her conduct to the Headmaster."

Beryl's face fell at that. She could see herself being kept in after school for the rest of the week.

"I was only tryin' on the tin suit to see what it felt like," Beryl protested, as the armour was taken off her. "It's part of learnin' history to find out what armour feels like. I don't see what's wrong in tryin' to learn history."

But it was no use arguing with Miss Primm. Beryl sighed resignedly. She could see she was for it.

After that she managed to keep out of trouble—at least, until Mr Widge led the party down to the dark dungeons underneath the castle. There he showed them a chamber containing ancient instruments of torture, including a rack.

"The unhappy victim was placed on this rack," stated the guide, with gloomy relish, "and his arms and legs were tied. Then a handle was turned, stretching the ropes tight, and they pulled his arms and legs until he felt most uncomfortable."

Miss Primm hastily suggested that they should pass on to something more cheerful, but Beryl hung behind. The rack sounded jolly interesting to her.

She managed to persuade Pudge Dawson, one of her class-mates, to help her find out if the rack still worked. She got Pudge fixed in the machine all right, but before she could start turning the handle, Miss Primm came back, which was very lucky for Pudge.

"Beryl!" screeched Miss Primm. "This is the last straw! Your behaviour is beyond endurance! Come with me!"

She grabbed the protesting Beryl by an ear and marched her along to an empty room.

"You're not going to look over any more of the castle!" snapped the angry teacher. "You will remain here, where you can't get into any more mischief, until the rest of the class has finished sight-seeing. Then we shall return to school and the Headmaster will deal with you as you deserve!"

Beryl glowered as Miss Primm stamped off, leaving her alone in the room. It was a large and gloomy room, with oak-panelled walls and practically bare of furniture.

"There's nothin' to do here," Beryl grumbled. "Jolly mean I call it, stickin' me in here with nothin' to do, while everybody else looks round the castle. An' I was only tryin' to learn about history—"

She suddenly broke off. She noticed a shelf above her head. Standing on it was a large bucket.

"I wonder what that bucket's doin' up there?" Beryl muttered. "It's a funny place to put a bucket. I wonder what's in it?"

Naturally, she had to find out. By standing on tip-toe, she was just able to reach the shelf. As she edged the bucket towards her with her finger-tips, it suddenly toppled.

Next moment—*swoosh!*—a white deluge descended on Beryl. She knew what was in the bucket now all right—whitewash! It smothered her from head to feet.

"Yugh!" gurgled Beryl, staggering back.

The whitewash dripped down her face. It was in her ears and in her eyes. Unable to see where she was going, she tottered round the room, hands outstretched.

She blundered against one of the panelled walls and suddenly there was a soft click. Next moment a panel had slid aside, revealing a dark opening.

By accident, Beryl had bumped against a hidden switch. The switch had opened the panel, which led to a secret passage. As Beryl, still unable to see, tumbled into the passage, the panel closed silently behind her.

The Man With The Mask

IT was some minutes before Beryl could wipe the whitewash out of her eyes. Then she had a look round and discovered that she was in a gloomy, brick-walled passage.

The secret panel was closed tight and she couldn't find the switch that opened it from the inside.

"Well, I've jolly well found the secret passage anyway," Beryl chirped, recovering her good humour. "Now I kin do some *real* explorin'."

She started along the gloomy passage, leaving a trail

Beryl wanted to find out what was in the bucket— but not this way!

of whitewash behind her. A little farther along, the passage branched off to another one and then another.

Beryl was beginning to wonder how she was going to find her way out into the open again, when suddenly she came to a heavy iron door. From the other side of the door she heard a clanking, rattling noise.

"Gosh, what's going on here, I wonder?" muttered Beryl to herself, and, finding the door unfastened, she cautiously pushed it open.

Then her eyes popped wide open in astonishment. She found herself gazing into a small, dimly-lit room. Crouching in a corner of the room, beside an open chest, was a villainous-looking man with narrow, foxy eyes.

Into the chest he was packing jewellery and other valuables, including several gold cups and diamond bracelets. Sticking out from his pocket was a burglar's jemmy and a black mask.

"A blinkin' burglar!" breathed Beryl, startled. "Why, those noises Miss Primm heard weren't made by a ghost at all. They must have been made by this crook moving his chest of loot about."

Beryl was quite right. The foxy-faced man was an ex-guide, who had turned burglar. He knew more about the castle's secret passages than anybody else, and he had been using them to store his plunder.

He couldn't have found a safer hiding place, for he could make as much noise as he liked, everybody

Dad is amazed—For once, Beryl's PRAISED!

believing that the noise was being caused by the supposed ghost.

He might have gone on using the place for years without being discovered, if Beryl hadn't accidentally tumbled into the secret passage.

"I'd better get out of here and tell the police," Beryl muttered to herself, but as she was turning away she bumped against the door, which swung wide open with a rusty squeak.

Beryl let out a howl of alarm as the burglar whirled round and spotted her. But before she could bolt, she was astonished to hear an even louder squawk of fright from the burglar.

"It's the ghost!" he bleated, gaping at Beryl in horror. "It's the White Knight!"

Beryl suddenly remembered that she was still smothered from head to feet in whitewash. Seeing her standing there in the gloomy doorway, the burglar had mistaken her for a spook.

Beryl seized her chance to put him to flight. She let out an ear-splitting moan and advanced into the room, waving her arms about.

"Help!" shrieked the burglar, losing his nerve completely and charging out through another door. "I—I never believed those old ghost stories until now!"

He tore along one of the secret passages in panic, hotly pursued by Beryl, who was still flapping her arms and wailing in a blood-curdling way.

For about ten minutes she chased the panic-stricken crook up and down the passages, until at last, breathless and scared out of his wits, he came to a secret panel, opened it, and stumbled out into a room.

Miss Primm and the rest of the class were being shown around the room by Mr Widge at the time. They had the shock of their lives when the panting burglar suddenly appeared before them.

"Save me from the ghost!" he howled, flopping down on his knees. "Call the police! Lock me up! Put me in some safe cell before the ghost gets me!"

Then Beryl popped out through the secret door. Miss Primm let out a startled shriek, but the light was better here and she suddenly recognised the "ghost."

"It's Beryl!" she spluttered.

Grinning, Beryl explained what had happened and Mr Widge sent for the police. Before the dazed burglar could recover, he was on his way to the police station.

But Beryl's Mum and Dad had an awful shock a little later. They were just about to have tea when they saw Beryl coming up the path to the house escorted by a couple of burly constables.

"She's got herself arrested now!" croaked Dad in horror. "What's the little imp been up to this time, I wonder?"

Prepared for the worst, he opened the door. To his surprise and relief, the two cops smiled at him.

"Your little girl is a real heroine," stated one of them, patting the smirking Beryl on the shoulder. "Thanks to her, we've been able to round up a burglar we've been after for months. We've just called to tell you that you should be proud of her."

Dad was too stunned to answer. Beryl not only escaped trouble at school, but she came in for a nice little reward as well. No wonder it took Dad a long, long time to recover!

"Save me from the ghost!" the burglar howled, as Beryl popped out after him through the secret door.

Fatty treats the "monster" to sweets!

THE DANDY

fun for boys and girls!

EVERY MONDAY

42p

No. 2711 November 6th, 1993.

— But he's a big hit as a spooky pumpkin!

THE DANDY

fun for boys and girls!

EVERY MONDAY

No. 2893 May 3rd, 1997

42p

What does Dan see that makes him flee?

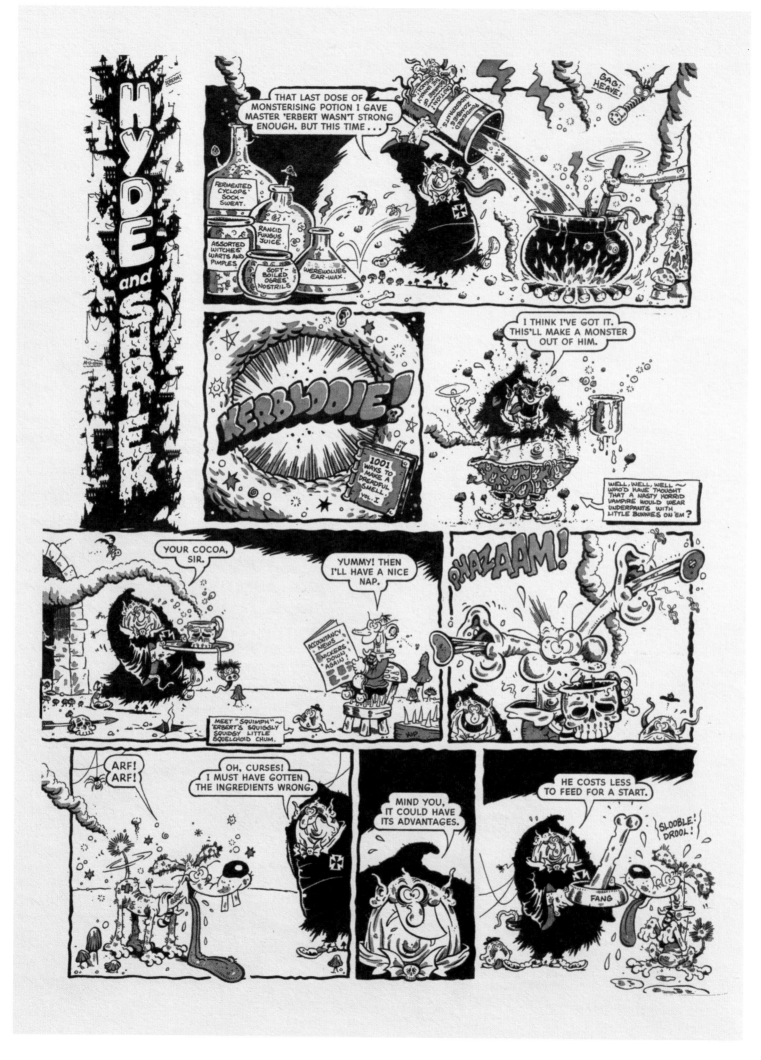

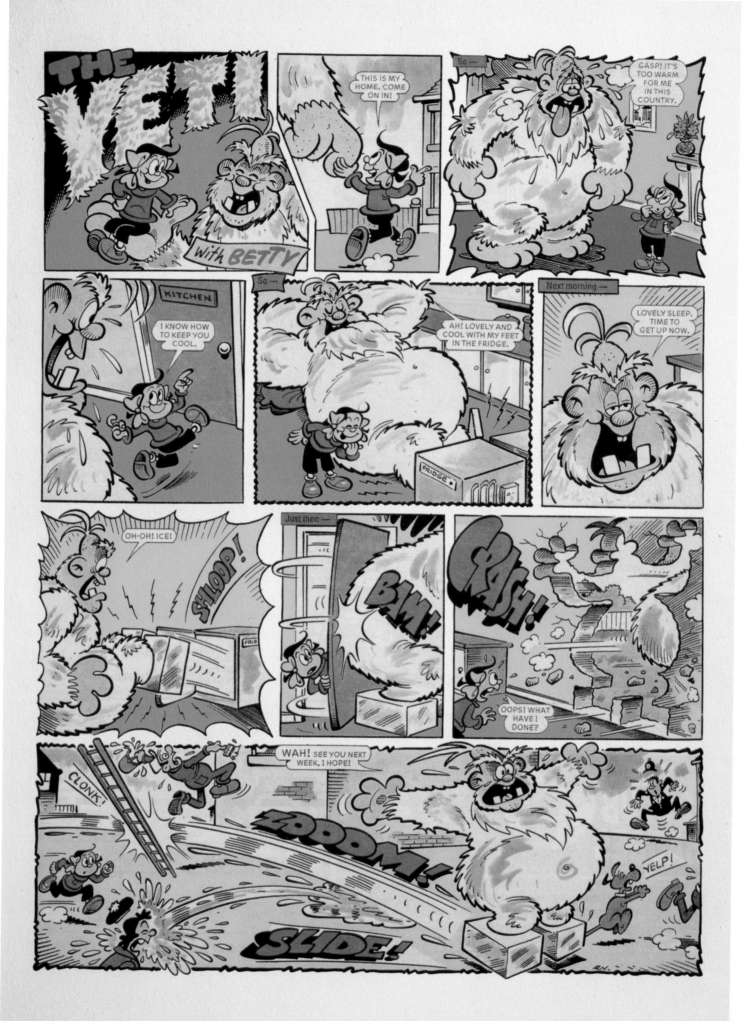

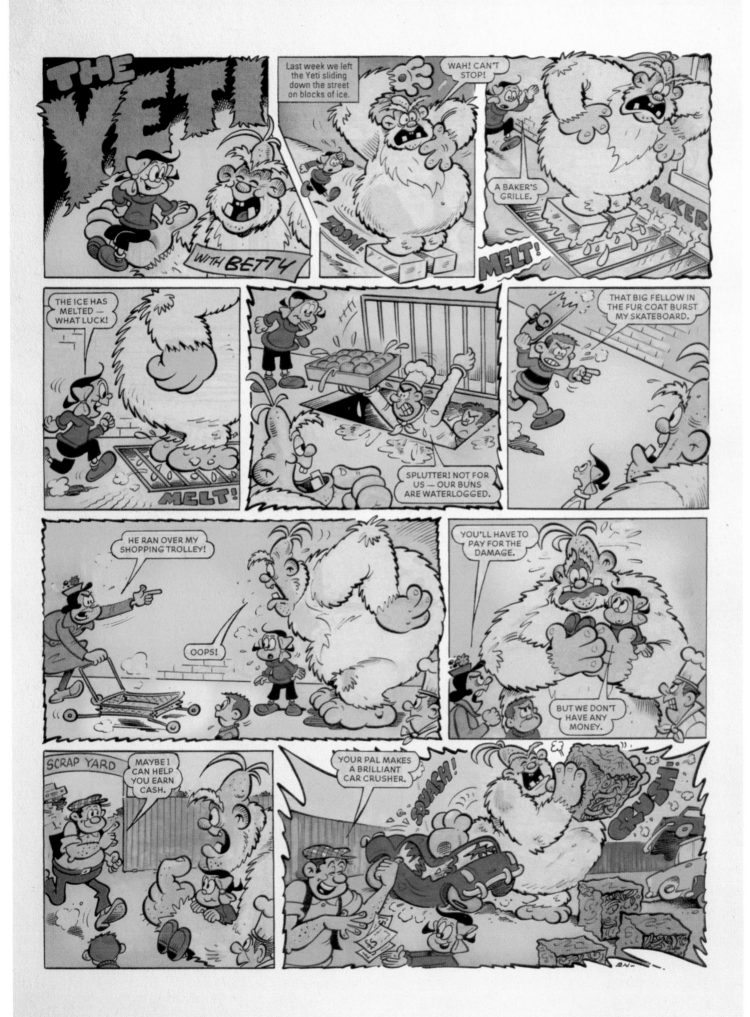

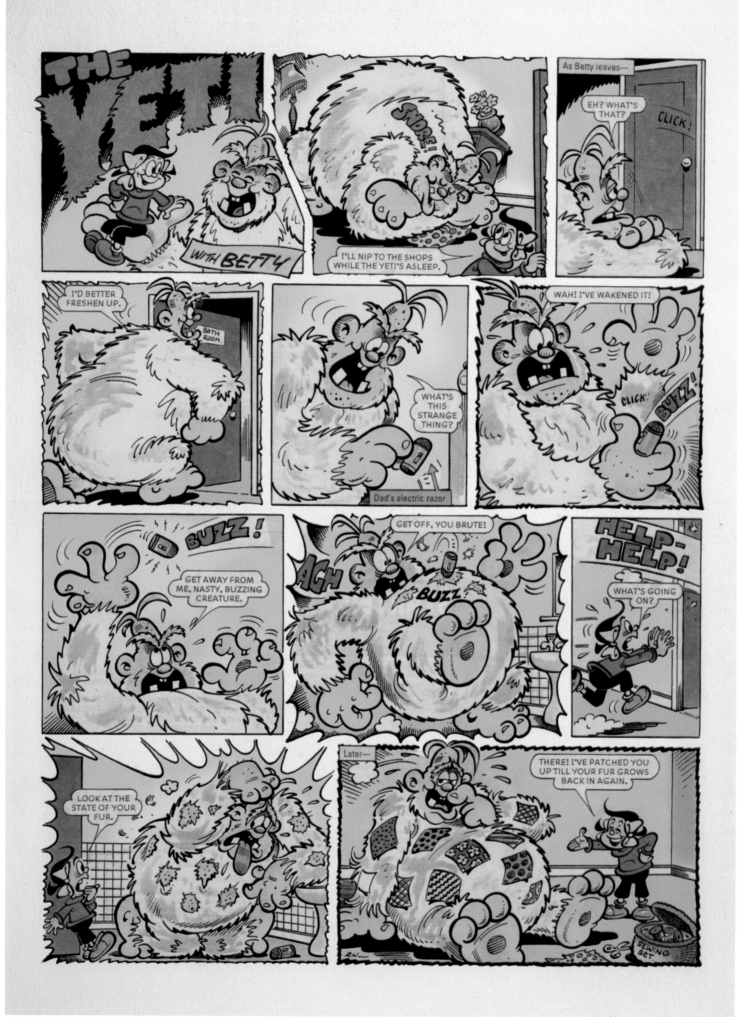

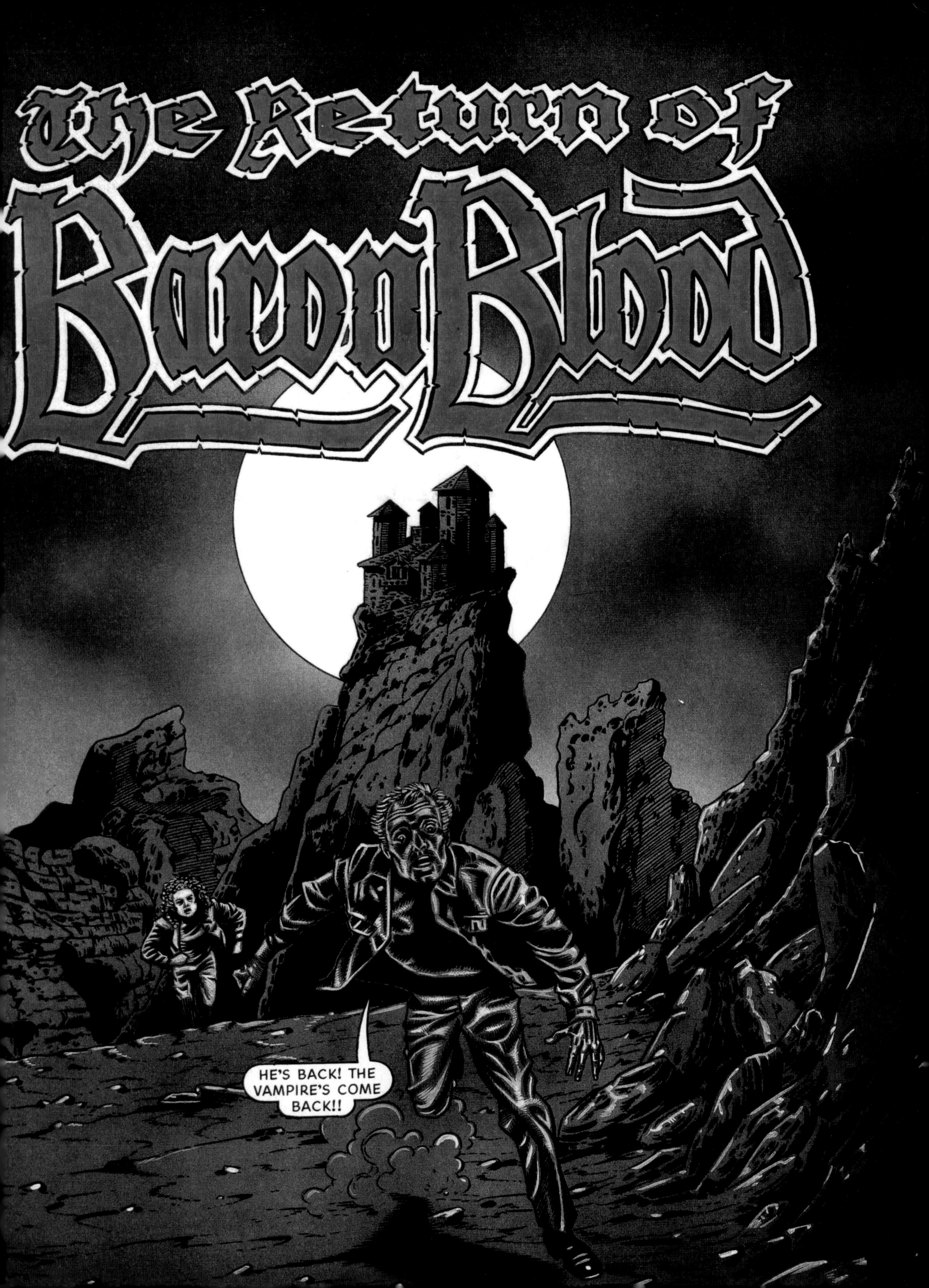
The Return of
Baron Blood
HE'S BACK! THE VAMPIRE'S COME BACK!!

The next day, at the dig headquarters —

I CAN'T BELIEVE IT! OF ALL THE SUPERSTITIOUS RUBBISH!

I'M SORRY, PROFESSOR DEWARS, BUT THE WORKERS ARE SCARED STIFF. THEY REFUSE TO SET FOOT IN THE CASTLE!

BUT THE DIG MUST CONTINUE! WE'RE SO CLOSE!

DAD, CALM DOWN. THERE'S NOTHING YOU CAN DO ABOUT THESE OLD SUPERSTITIONS.

MAYBE I CAN'T, LUCY. BUT I KNOW SOMEONE WHO CAN.

IS THAT WHO YOU'RE GOING TO CALL?

YES. PROFESSOR COTFORD IS AN OLD FRIEND OF MINE. HE'S ALSO AN EXPERT ON SUPERSTITIONS AND THE SUPERNATURAL.

I'LL PROVE TO THEM THAT THERE'S NO SUCH THING AS A VAMPIRE. THEN WE CAN GET BACK TO WORK.

Days pass, until —

HELLO? I'M SORRY. MY DAD'S NOT HERE AT THE MOMENT . . . OKAY. I'LL TELL HIM.

THERE'S A LIGHT ON IN THE CASTLE. THAT MUST BE DAD. I'D BETTER TELL HIM THE PROFESSOR WILL BE ARRIVING TONIGHT.

And —

THERE HE IS.

DAD?

GOOD EVENING, MY CHILD. SHOULD YOU BE OUT SO LATE?

OH!!

SORRY. I WAS LOOKING FOR MY DAD. HAVE YOU SEEN HIM?

I HAVEN'T SEEN A SINGLE SOUL. I'VE ONLY JUST ARRIVED.

OF COURSE! HE'S THE PROFESSOR.

YOU'RE THE VAMPIRE EXPERT, AREN'T YOU?

NOT AN EXPERT, NO. BUT I DO KNOW OF SUCH THINGS. ARE YOU HAVING PROBLEMS WITH VAMPIRES?

Lucy explains and —

SO, THE SCIENTISTS REFUSE TO DIG BECAUSE THEY ARE AFRAID OF THIS SO-CALLED VAMPIRE?

YOU MEAN YOU DON'T BELIEVE IN BARON WALPURGIS?

OH, YES. I KNOW THE STORY OF BARON WALPURGIS.

THE BARON LIVED AND DIED IN THIS CASTLE, TWO CENTURIES BEFORE YOU WERE BORN.

HE WAS A CRUEL AND WICKED MAN. HE LIKED NOTHING BETTER THAN TO TERRORISE THE VILLAGERS.

SO CRUEL WAS HE THAT, WHEN HE DIED, HE WAS CURSED TO ROAM THE EARTH ... AS A VAMPIRE.

AND HE BECAME KNOWN IN LOCAL LEGENDS AS BARON BLOOD!

AND HE'S STILL TERRORISING PEOPLE?

IF IT IS REALLY HIM.

BUT, AFTER ALL THESE YEARS, THE BARON WOULD BE TIRED OF FRIGHTENING PEOPLE.

HE WOULD JUST WANT TO BE LEFT IN PEACE, FAR AWAY FROM THIS PLACE.

BUT WHY WOULD ANYONE ELSE WANT TO SCARE PEOPLE AWAY?

Meanwhile—

DAD! OW! WHAT'S THIS?

MAKE-UP WHITE

THE PROFESSOR WAS RIGHT. SOMEONE IS TRYING TO SCARE EVERYONE AWAY.

I'D BETTER... HEY!!

SSSSSSH... LOOK!

YOU'D BETTER GET INTO COSTUME IN CASE ANYONE COMES BACK.

DON'T WORRY. WE'LL KEEP THEM SCARED AWAY UNTIL WE FIND THAT GOLD.

WE'VE GOT TO GET THE POLICE, PROFESSOR... PROFESSOR?

The End.

Eddie Potter is an ordinary schoolboy. In fact he's the only ordinary schoolboy at an extraordinary school for ghouls.

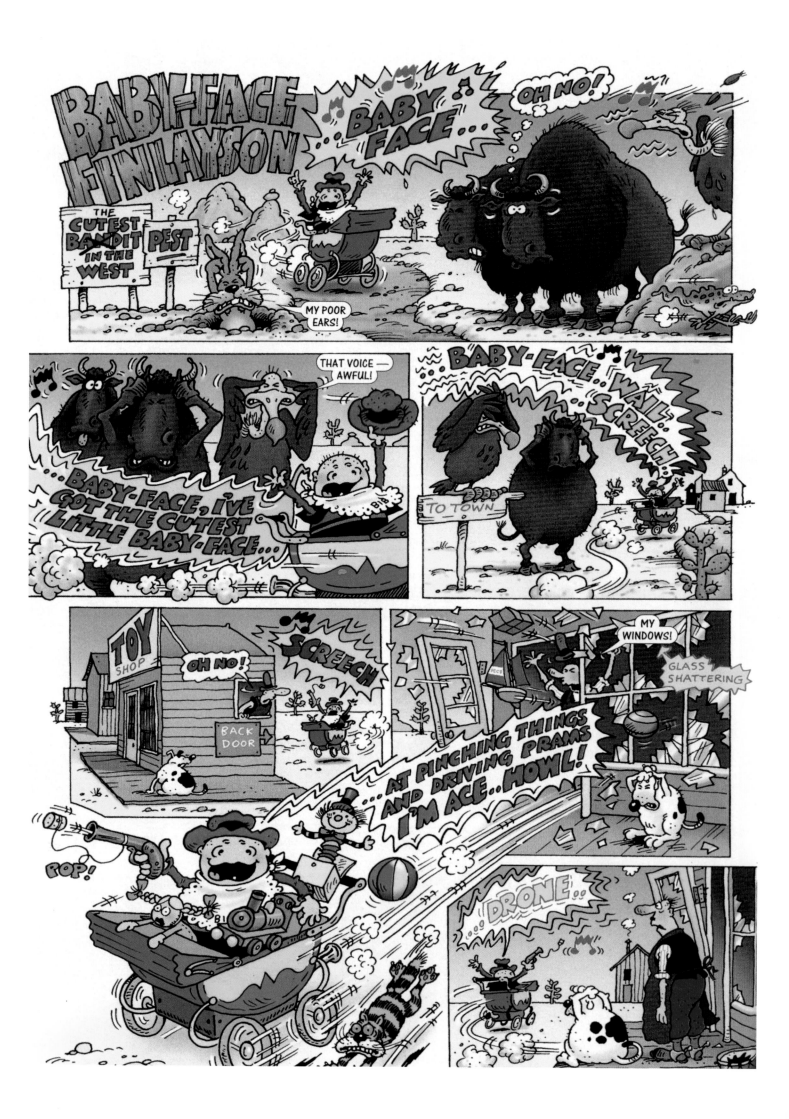

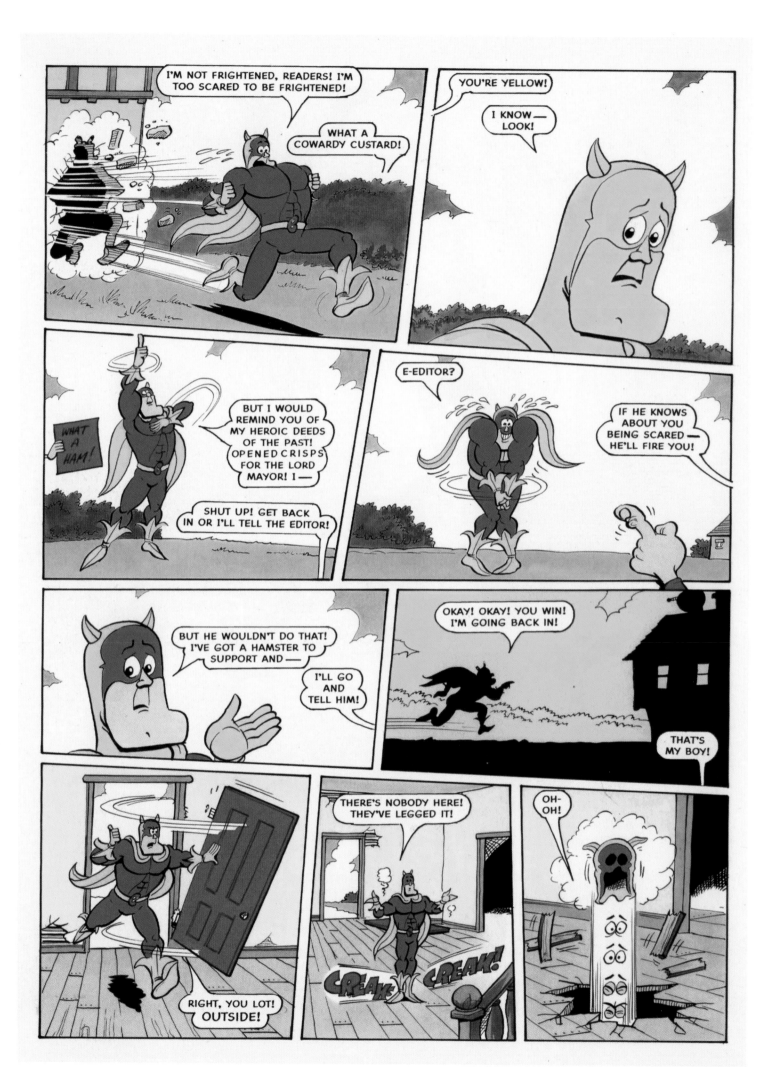

SNEAKER

ALL THESE STRANGE THINGS HAPPENING LATELY . . .

THIS OAR DIDN'T BREAK. IT WAS CUT!

THANKS FOR GETTING YOUR MODELS TO HELP, JUMBO. GRANDPA'S GOT LOTS OF MODELS IN THE COTTAGE.

And . . .

THIS IS CAPTAIN BLUEBRISTLE'S PRIVATEER, "THE WOLFHAWK".

SHE WERE A TREASURE SHIP, RUN AGROUND BY WRECKERS NEARLY TWO-HUNDRED YEARS AGO. ALL THAT'S LEFT ARE HER RIBS A-STICKIN' OUT OF THE SAND DOWN ON OUR BEACH.

THE TREASURE WAS NEVER FOUND BUT GRANDPA BELIEVES THAT ON STORMY NIGHTS, THE GHOST OF BLUEBRISTLE STILL HAUNTS THESE SHORES, FOREVER SEARCHING FOR HIS LOST GOLD.

WOW! COOL STORY.

Soon . . .

UH-OH! HERE COMES TROUBLE. IT'S ARCH STANTON, THE PROPERTY DEVELOPER WHO'S BEEN TRYING TO PERSUADE GRANDPA TO SELL OUR COTTAGE.

IS THAT RIGHT? HMM . . .

Special Spooky Guest Dr. Beastly

With a tale of the slightly unpleasant.

Greetings, revolting readers. It's your old fiend, Dr Beastly here, with a terrifyingly tortuous tale to darken down even the brightest Hallowe'en.

It's a strange old story of a strange old house with a strange old library full of strange old secrets. I call it...

...THE TALE OF THE TOMES FULL OF TALES FROM THE TOMB!

Professor Dodgerson, an expert on great historical dodges, scams and tricks, had inherited a gloomy mansion house from a long-lost relative.

Good grief! An old ruin like this is just the place for an archaeologist like me. I might even dig up some jokes to use in this story.

Opening a door that creaked like a long-shut coffin lid, the Professor caught his first glimpse of the cobweb-strewn interior of the dusty old mansion.

CREAK!

A scream rang out! Had his intrusion in this shunned and lonely spot awakened some long-dead spirit or summoned some unearthly guardian?

SCREAM!

Oh, no, nothing like that. It's just that I hate tidying and this place doesn't need a ghost-buster, it needs a dust-buster!

Fortunately, before this could turn into an episode of "How Clean Is Your Haunted House", with demonic dusting and horrific hoovering, the Professor located the loathsome library.

LIBRARY

CREAK!

Now, this is more like it. These books are bound to have a dodge or two to add to my collection.

HELL HOUNDS

Here's hoping the first dodge I find is a dodge to get out of having to search through all of these books for dodges, though.

Mind you, if I investigate, I might find a clue to my long-lost relative's disappearance, and the treasure he was supposed to have hidden.

A BLOW FOR FREEDOM

A BLOW FOR FREEDOM

THE WOMAN IN BLACK & WHITE

"Knowest thou, gentle reader, that the cursed house of Dodgerson is surrounded by legends of blood chilling horror." Hmm... Cheerful start.

A BLOW FOR FREEDOM

"Let the tale of the treasure hunter, Professor Dennistoun, and what he discovered, stand as a warning to the curious..."

A BLOW

Could this mysterious metal cylinder I have unearthed be the whistle that summons the legendary phantom hound?

That can only be a howl of unearthly horror...

HOOOWL!

BLOW!

Oh, pants! Or, since it's Victorian times, oh, long-johns! It isn't a whistle. It's an old pea-shooter.

It's bad enough living next to haunted houses and graveyards without being shelled with peas!

SNATCH!

Maybe this'll tell me something more helpful.

I wouldn't bet on it!

PROFESSOR PLUGSTON

THE MUMMY

THE DADDY

THE GRANNY

THE CHERRY MONKEY'S PAW

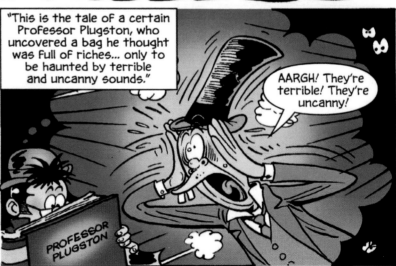

"This is the tale of a certain Professor Plugston, who uncovered a bag he thought was full of riches... only to be haunted by terrible and uncanny sounds."

AARGH! They're terrible! They're uncanny!

PROFESSOR PLUGSTON

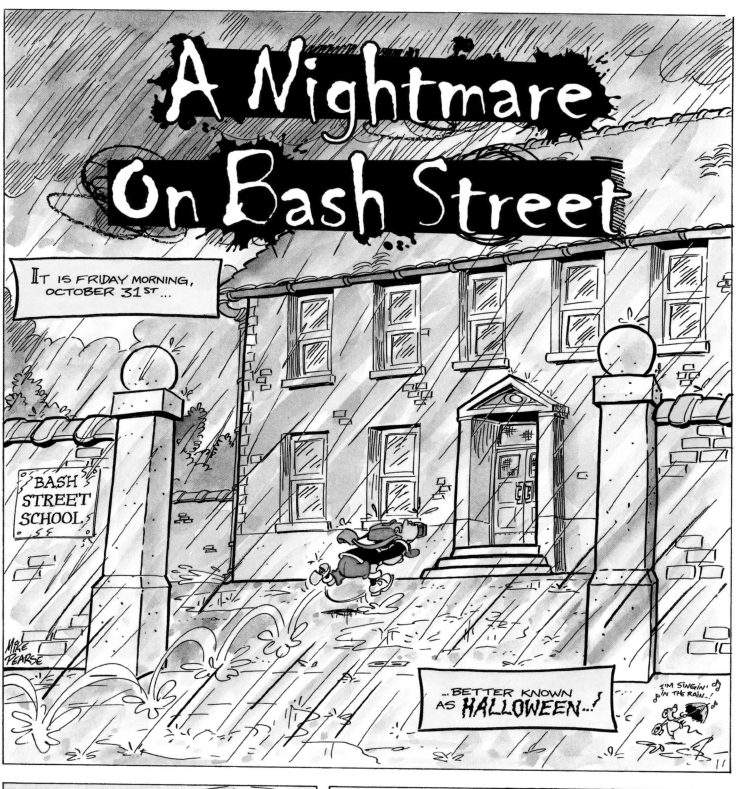

A Nightmare On Bash Street

IT IS FRIDAY MORNING, OCTOBER 31ST...

BASH STREET SCHOOL

MIKE PEARSE

...BETTER KNOWN AS HALLOWEEN...!

I'M SINGIN' IN THE RAIN...!

...SO YOU'LL BE THERE TONIGHT?

OF COURSE, HEADMASTER!

AND YOU HAVE WHAT WE NEED?

IT'S ALL IN HERE!

PAT! PAT!

HMM ... I WONDER WHAT'S IN TEACHER'S BAG ?!

2B

AARGH!

SOMEBODY'S COMING !

COR BLIMEY, 'ERBERT! WHICH GENIUS PUT *YOU* ON LOOK-OUT DUTY ?!

SAY NO MORE.

PHEW! FALSE ALARM !

YEAH, IT WAS ONLY DANNY !

WHAT ARE YOU ALL DOING ROUND TEACHER'S DESK ?

WE'RE PLANNING A FEW LITTLE SURPRISES FOR HIM...

MOUSE TRAP

AARGH!

SOMEBODY'S COMING !

'ERBERT, ONE OF THESE DAYS I'M GOING TO...

HEY! WHAT ARE YOU LOT DOING ROUND MY DESK ?!

ER ... JUST MAKING SURE IT'S ALL RIGHT !

YEAH!...GOOD SOLID WOOD THIS !

WELL, PLUG, I THINK THE SAFETY CHECK PROVES...

TO YOUR SEATS... ...NOW !

THUMP!

STOMP! STOMP!

2

LATER, DURING LUNCH-BREAK IN THE STAFF ROOM...

SLAM!

CRASH!

WHY, TEACHER— WHAT'S THE MATTER?

OH, THE KIDS WERE A NIGHTMARE THIS MORNING!

PYOING!

TEA

I ♥ TEA

CONFISCATED TOYS

CONFISCATED PETS

THE BEANO

...I'M NOT SURE HOW MUCH MORE BAD BEHAVIOUR I CAN TAKE!

OH, CHEER UP! DON'T FORGET, WE'RE GOING TO A HALLOWEEN PARTY AT LORD SNOBBINGTON'S TONIGHT!

OH, THAT REMINDS ME...

YOU'D BEST GIVE THIS TO THE SEWING TEACHER SO SHE'LL HAVE TIME TO MAKE OUR OUTFITS.

HOW TO BE A WIZARD BY ALI KAZAM

THUMP!

WOW! THIS IS FULL OF GREAT PICTURES!

YES! WE'LL HAVE THE BEST COSTUMES AT THE PARTY!

HOW TO BE A WIZARD BY ALI KAZAM

I'LL TAKE THIS TO HER RIGHT AWAY!

THANK GOODNESS..!

TEACHER'S TRAINING TO BE A WIZARD?!

THE BEANO

⑤

AFTER LUNCH-BREAK...

WE'RE OFF TO SEE THE WIZARD! THE WONDERFUL WIZARD OF OZ! HE REALLY IS...

ALL RIGHT! ...ALL RIGHT!

...HOW MANY TIMES HAVE I WARNED YOU NOT TO RUN INSIDE THE SCHOOL BUILDING, SIMON?

CROAK!

DON'T ANSWER BACK OR I'LL TURN YOU INTO SOMETHING WORSE!

NOW HOP ALONG TO YOUR CLASS AND WAIT FOR THE SPELL TO WEAR OFF!

...AND DON'T LET ME CATCH YOU RUNNING INDOORS AGAIN.!

CROAK!

WHAT ARE YOU LOT STARING AT?

NOTHING, SIR!

JUST ON OUR WAY INTO THE CLASSROOM! HEH! HEH!

THWAP!

2B

ER... COULD YOU UNLOCK THE DOOR, SIR?

YES, OF COURSE!

OOOOH... ...PRETTY!

SNAP!

CLICK!

WELL, GO ON IN...THE DOOR WON'T BITE YOU..!

7

INSIDE THE CLASSROOM...

RIGHT, LET ME FIND A PEN AND I'LL TAKE THE AFTERNOON REGISTER.

WHERE ARE YOU GONNA..?

...GLUMF!

IS THERE A PROBLEM?

A PROBLEM, SIR?

OH BOTHER! MY PEN DOESN'T WORK!

GO PUT YOURSELF INTO THE BIN, YOU NAUGHTY PEN!

HOP! HOP! KERPLONK!

HOW DID TEACHER DO THIS?...WAIT AND SEE!

NOW, HERE ARE THE TEXT-BOOKS FOR TODAY'S HISTORY LESSON...

HISTORY
HISTORY
HISTORY
HISTORY
HISTORY
HISTORY

HISTORY WITH NO PICTURES

...AND I SINCERELY HOPE...

...THAT YOU ARE ALL GOING TO PAY FULL ATTENTION!

YES...

OF COURSE...

...NICE BOOK!

...BECAUSE IF YOU DON'T PAY FULL ATTENTION...

...I'M GOING TO GET VERY... ...VERY... ANGRY!

HA! HA! HA! HA! HA! HA! HA!

8

AT HOME-TIME...

SHEESH! THAT WAS THE WORST LESSON OF MY *LIFE*!

YEAH! I SPENT THE WHOLE AFTERNOON *WORKING*!

NOW DO YOU BELIEVE ME?!

HEY, DANNY... ...LOOK!

UH-OH! I HOPE THAT POINTY THING IS NOT WHAT I THINK IT IS!

WOW! A PERFECT FIT!

YES! AND I'VE JUST HAD A MARVELLOUS IDEA!

THUMP!

IF YOU TAKE ME TO THE PARTY IN *YOUR* CAR ...

...THEN I WON'T HAVE TO PUT ANY PETROL IN *MINE*!

A BRILLIANT NOTION, HEAD-MASTER...

ISN'T IT JUST?!

...I'LL SEE YOU AT EIGHT!

EEK! TEACHER'S COMING THIS WAY!

QUICK! ACT LIKE YOU'RE NOT SPYING ON HIM!

OooooH! WHAT A LOVELY POSTBOX!

YEAH!

HMM...

..ER... RED, ISN'T IT?

VERY...!

SOMETIMES, I WORRY ABOUT THOSE KIDS!

⑨

MEANWHILE ...

...SO, TEACHER, HOW DID YOU CONVINCE YOUR CLASS THAT YOU WERE A WIZARD?

CLANG!

I PLAYED A FEW TRICKS ON THEM!

LIKE WHAT?

WELL, FOR EXAMPLE, I TIED INVISIBLE FISHING LINE TO MY PEN...

...AND WHEN WINSTON, WHO WAS HIDING IN THE BIN, PULLED THE OTHER END THE PEN SEEMED TO COME ALIVE!

YOU SHOULD HAVE SEEN THE KIDS' FACES!

...IT WAS A PICTURE, HEADMASTER!

HA! HA! HA!

I'LL BET!

HO! HO! HO!

PING!

HA! HA! HA! HA! HA!

HO! HO! HO! HO! HO! HO! HO!

TURB

SNOBBINGTON MANOR

CLOING! CLOING! CLOING!

FIVE MINUTES LATER...

WHEW! WE'VE NEARLY CAUGHT UP WITH HIM!

IT'S A GOOD JOB TEACHER DRIVES LIKE AN OLD GRANNY!

I HEARD THAT!

SQUEEAK! SQUEEAK!

UH-OH! THE ROAD GOES RIGHT, BUT THE TYRE TRACKS GO LEFT!

DANNY...

...I HAVE A BA-A-AD FEELING ABOUT THIS!

12

13

16

19

AND SO, OUR STORY ENDS WITH EVERYONE ENJOYING THE HALLOWEEN BARBECUE...

THE END

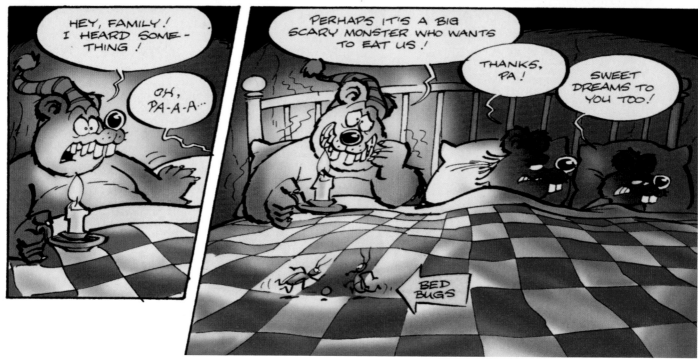

So that's a wrap — a mummy's wrap that is!
We hope you weren't too terrified by our unearthing of
some of the The Dandy and Beano's most spooktacular
strips! Fangs for joining our malevolent menaces as
they indulged in scarily-good frightening fun at the
expense of any poor souls who stayed up
past their bedtimes!

And on that note, we hope you'll be able to
sleep tonight!